Composition
&
Sketchbook II

(1/2" Ruled for 1st-2nd Grade Students)

MEMORIA PRESS

www.MemoriaPress.com

COMPOSITION & SKETCHBOOK
1/2″ Ruled for 1st-2nd Grade Students

BOOK TWO

ISBN 978-1-930953-88-8

First Edition © 2005 Memoria Press

Table of Contents

Composition and Sketchbook

This simple, well-planned book allows the student to continue practicing the skills presented in the Memoria Press *Copybook* sequence with additional Scripture, poetry, or composition selections. Designed to be used with or after *Copybook III*, the transitional line size and spacing of the *Composition and Sketchbook* prepare the young child for standard notebook paper. This valuable intermediate design requires the student to manage a blank page, a considerable task that requires practice, while accounting for small hands and beginner status. The opportunity to draw a picture illustrating each entry provides the perfect companion to copybook; drawing pages are included on each facing page. In years to come, these books will provide a treasured journal of the child's progress.

What is Copybook?

Copybook, like memorization, is a forgotten skill in modern education. However, like memorization, copybook is a beginning skill that is indispensable to the development of good language skills.

In *Copybook*, students practice penmanship, spelling, reading comprehension, punctuation, and vocabulary. Students develop the habits of accuracy, neatness, attention to detail, and patience; they practice correct grammar and good writing style; they develop an appreciation for what is good, noble, and beautiful in literature.

Copybook is not the only way for the young student to practice each of these skills—but it is the only exercise that develops all of them at the same time. Copybook is concrete and physical; it complements and completes the mental exercise of memorization and reading. Copybook is so simple and obvious that we often overlook it.

Even though penmanship is hard work for the young student, he should come to delight in the physical act of creating a beautiful page of writing. Because the student is not burdened by trying to compose his own words, he is liberated to concentrate on copying the immortal words of others. The young student who is not able to think great thoughts of his own can grow in wisdom by thinking great thoughts of others. After the discipline of copybook he can exercise his imagination and creativity; the original drawings of children are the perfect companion to copybook.

How to Use This Book

What to write is just as important as how to write. Not only do we want our littlest ones to form beautiful letters, we want them to copy beautiful words. Selecting quality content for introductory copy and composition work is an important task; students must develop an ear for great literature and language from their earliest years. The Memoria Press *Copybooks I-III* present close to one hundred beautiful quotes and poetry. This *Composition and Sketchbook* allows you to add your own literary finds to our priceless selections or use the blank lined pages for beginner composition works.

Like the Memoria Press *Copybooks*, the *Composition and Sketchbook* allows students to practice penmanship, spelling, reading comprehension, punctuation, and vocabulary. Students develop the habits of accuracy, neatness, attention to detail, and patience; they practice correct grammar and good writing style; they develop an appreciation for great works.

As with all instruction, the first task of the teacher is to communicate the importance of the lesson to the student and to model enthusiasm. The child should see copybook or composition as an opportunity to give his very best effort in penmanship and artwork throughout the year. Students should be inspired to produce quality work because the words they are asked to memorize and copy are great works. The quality of the work will be a direct reflection of the ability of the teacher to motivate the child to excellence.

How to Select Passages

When selecting supplemental copybook work, choose passages that are picturesque and filled with clear, rich language. Pull out memorable lines from the student's literature or select poems or passages from a children's classic poetry anthology. Always use history's best authors and books to train the student to appreciate and recognize great literature.

Composition

Students who have been nurtured on beautiful language will develop a desire to express their own thoughts and ideas. Remember that students who are just starting to compose thoughts for paper need much guidance. Writing in the early years should always be a supervised activity so students never develop poor composition habits. Narrative and descriptive responses to memorable literature serve as ideal beginner composition exercises. After a passage is read aloud and discussed, ask students to describe in detail a scene, a character, or an event. Vocabulary specific to the text should be placed on the board. Teachers should also suggest and post pertinent verbs, nouns, and adjectives so the student learns to use these parts of speech correctly and form complete and interesting sentences. By developing a sentence or composition together, the process of composing original thoughts is modeled for the child, and the burden of filling an empty page is lifted. Once completed, it is especially important to review the student's composition so errors are promptly identified and corrected.

Always maintain high standards for students using this book. Papers should always be neat, with words spelled correctly and punctuation exact. Students should copy passages precisely or present well-ordered original compositions. Use this *Composition and Sketchbook* to train students to consistently produce high-quality papers, worthy of a teacher's time and talent.

Line and Letter Practice

We have found that little instruction is necessary to teach basic letter strokes. Instead, it is "practice, practice, practice" on words and passages that creates neat and proficient writers.

Letter Practice Overview

Do not underestimate a young student's ability to create simple strokes and stay within the lines. Always encourage straight lines, round circles, and appropriately sized letters. Once the basic strokes are mastered, your student should be able to make every letter in the alphabet.

It is not necessary to practice each letter over and over until it is perfect, just until your student has the basic ability to form letters correctly. The purpose of copybook work is to allow your student to practice handwriting on great passages, not lists of letters. You will notice significant improvements in letter formation as the year progresses.

Student Guidelines

1. Students should hold pencils properly.

Left-handed   Right-handed

2. Start each line close to the left margin and don't cross the right margin.

3. Uppercase letters must touch the top and bottom lines.

4. Most lowercase letters start at the middle, dashed line.

5. Lowercase b, d, f, h, k, t, and l are all tall letters that touch the top line.

6. Lowercase g, j, p, q, and y have hooks or tails that cross the bottom line.

7. All words should be one pinky space apart.

8. Letters should all stand tall and straight.

9. Erase mistakes completely and be neat.